A KENT BOOK

What memorial is this, and where is it?

Illustrations by the author

Alan Major

S. B. Publications

By the same author

A New Dictionary of Kent Dialect. Meresborough Books
Whose Buried Where in Kent. Meresborough Books
Hidden Kent. Countryside Books
Cherries in the Rise. S. B. Publications
Goldings, Napoleons and Romneys. S. B. Publications
The Kentish Lights, S.B.Publications

First published in 2000 by S. B. Publications,
19 Grove Road, Seaford, East Sussex BN25 1TP

ISBN 1 85770 165 8

Designed and typeset by CGB, Lewes
Printed by MFP Design and Print
Longford Trading Estate, Stretford,
Manchester M32 0JT

CONTENTS

Front cover question: It is not a trick pic, the ground floor frontage is really leaning to the right. Why – and where is it?

Back cover question: What is the structure adjoining the Georgian mansion which overlooks the Medway and is now used as local government offices?

INTRODUCTION

Quiz book compilers give the appearances of being know-alls because they have the answers in front of them before they pose the questions. This is not quite the case, as I found in preparing this book. I did know the basic answers, but often discovered fascinating additional facts that increased my knowledge of the county. I hope that with the questions and answers in this book that also happens to you.

It has been my intention to provide a wide enough range of subjects to ensure that readers are likely to have a working knowledge of at least some of them. It is not all history and local know-how, nor full of questions that can be answered only by the oldest inhabitant with a brilliantly sharp memory. There is, hopefully, something here for everyone including new residents of the county who, no doubt, are already aware that true-born Men of Kent and Women of Kent are born east of the Medway and Kentish Men and and Kentish Women are born west of the Medway. Now remember that – for any references to Kentish Men and Men of Kent that crop up in the questions are likely to have some locational significance. There may be a clue, too, in the illustration at the top of each page.

If you are totally stumped for an answer they are all at the back of the book but please, play the game and only look at the answers after you have tried the questions in the individual sections.

Alan Major, (Man of Kent)
Canterbury
Autumn 1999

1 KENT BOOK OF RECORDS

My dear I am always nervous about doing something for the first time.
Dame Gwen Ffrangcon-Davies on facing death at 101.

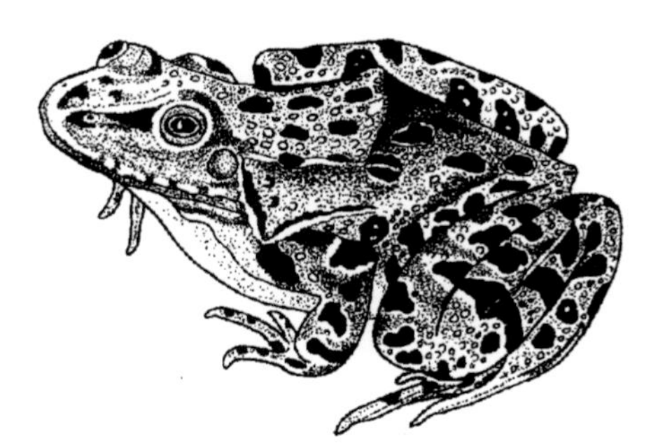

1 What world 'first' was issued at the original Canterbury West railway terminus – and when ?
2 Britain's first motor show was held here in 1895. Apparently all who visited it were enthusiastic, no one was disgusted?
3 Where, on 25 July 1909, did Bleriot land after completing the first cross-Channel flight?
4 Which fruit was cultivated for the first time commercially at Teynham?
5 In 1898 the first wireless message was transmitted from a Kent lighthouse to a ship at sea. Which lighthouse was it?
6 Where, in 1725, (some say 1729) was an electric current first made to travel a distance of some 800 feet – along a 'string' supported on silk threads between two poles.
7 In which Kent seaside town is there a public theatre with the world's smallest stage?
8 A pond at Oxney was the first home in 1935 of Britain's largest frog. What frog is it and to what size does the female of the species grow?
9 In which Kent church is the county's finest collection of monumental brasses?
10 Sir Hiram Maxim's aeroplane was the first heavier than air machine ever known to work. It ran on rails. Where?

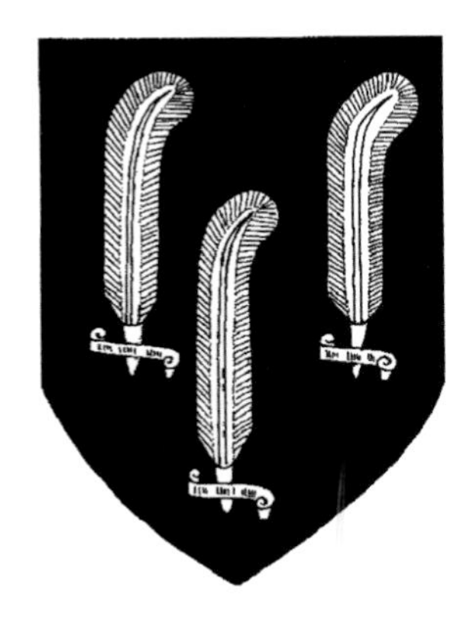

2 FAMOUS MEN

'Let us now praise famous men'
Men of little showing –
For their work continueth,
And their work continueth,
Broad and deep continueth,
Greater than their knowing!

School song from *Stalky and Co* by Rudyard Kipling

1 Who was the acerbic Irish playwright who visited Broadstairs in 1899 and sent a postcard saying that after ten minutes there he was 'bored beyond description' and went on to describe Margate as 'a most dismal hole?

2 Name the eighteenth century engineer/inventor who has a window in Westminster Abbey and a tablet with his portrait and picture of his steam engine in Dartford church?

3 What honour did Gillingham confer on First World War air ace, Major J B 'Mick' McCudden VC, on 4 June 1918?

4 The discovery of what is Folkestone born William Harvey's claim to fame?

5 This Kentish greengrocer, in the ketch Lively Lady, was the first Englishman to sail around the world single-handed. Name him?

6 Which of the Rolling Stones was born at Dartford?

7 Who was the arbiter of taste who was Master of Ceremonies at Tunbridge Wells for a quarter of a century from 1735?

8 Who was the sixteenth century lawyer, statesman and saint (he was canonised in 1935) whose head is buried in the Roper family vault in St Dunstan's church, Canterbury?

9 Who was the bishop of Rochester, also canonised in 1935 – and beheaded by Henry VIII?

10 The holder of the world land and water speed records in the 1930s is buried in St Nicholas churchyard, Chislehurst. His name?

3 CHURCHES

Halloa! Here's a church! . . . Let's go in! . . .Here's Miss Skiffins! Let's have a wedding.

Wemmick in Charles Dickens'*Great Expectations.*

1 The churchyard at Kemsing has a 'crinkle-crankle' wall. What is it and when was it built?

2 Which church is known as 'The Barn of Kent'?

3 What is the link between All Saints church, Maidstone, and the USA?

4 What is unusual about the bell tower of Brookland church?

5 St Andrews church, Shepherdswell, has a rare palimpsest. What is a palimpsest?

6 In the Tudor vestry of St Bartholomew's church, Otford, is a wafer oven. For what was it used?

7 Which Kent church has Swiss scenes in some of its windows?

8 The mechanism of the clock in which Kent church was the prototype for Big Ben?

9 St Leonard's church, Hythe, has an ossuary which is open to the public at certain times. What would visitors see there?

10 Why is the Church of King Charles the Martyr at Tunbridge Wells, named after an English king and not a saint?

4 MIXED BAG

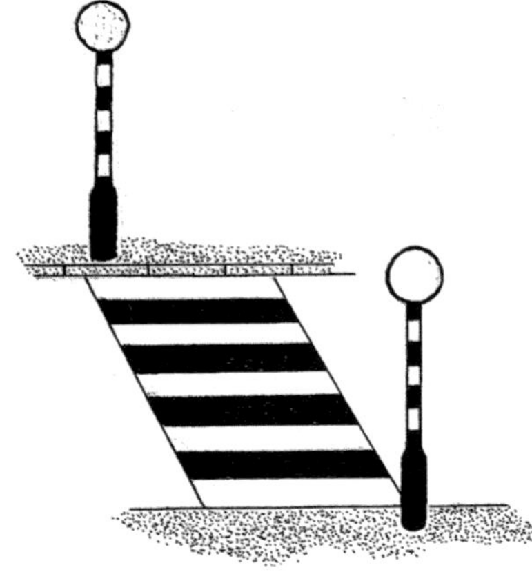

It couldn't exist without allongong or marshonging to something or other.
Charles Dickens. *Hard Times*,

1 Leslie Hore-Belisha lived at Eynsford. To what did he give his name in September, 1934?

2 Who wrote: 'We all are with you now from shore to shore: Ye Men of Kent, 'Tis Victory or Death' and what was the title of the poem?

3 What and where was the 'Babies Castle'?

4 Who was the Kent sculptor and artist who lived near Littlebourne and did seventy two carvings for the liners *Queen Mary* and the *Queen Elizabeth?*

5 You need a horse to use a jossing block. Why?

6 For what is Romney Marsh world famous?

7 Which village has a church with the unusual dedication – The Church of the Beheading of St John the Baptist?

8 The rules of the Jesus Hospital, Northgate, Canterbury, founded for 'a warden, seven poor brothers, four poor sisters' in 1595 state: 'no domestic animal shall be kept by a brother or sister except . . .' What is the exception – and why?

9 William Pett, 1710-1786, lived at Sevenoaks, where the Vine is reputed to be the oldest cricket ground in Kent and Pett the earliest known maker of what ?

10 What was the fish caught in the Medway by a Strood fisherman in 1870, put on ice and delivered to Queen Victoria at Windsor Castle?

5 MUSIC AND MUSICIANS

An unalterable and unquestioned law of the musical world required that the German text of French operas sung by Swedish artists should be translated into Italian for the clear understanding of English speaking audiences.

Edith Wharton
The Age of Innocence.

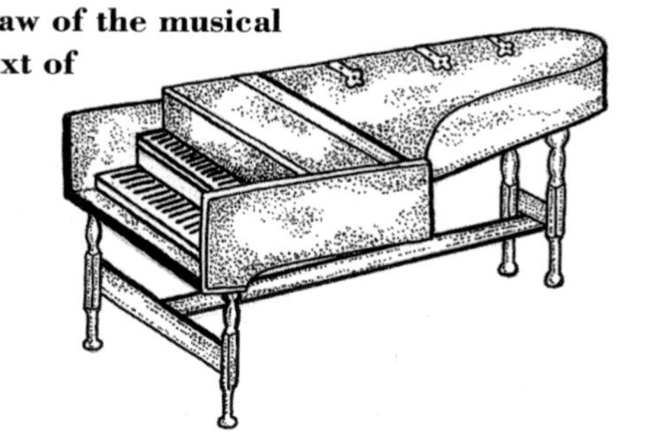

1 Who composed his famous *Capriol Suite* in 1926 while living in Eynsford?
2 What caused the death of organist and composer Orlando Gibbons, who visited Canterbury in 1625 to play at the wedding of Charles I and Henrietta Maria of France?
3 And where did his mourning wife have him buried?
4 John Ireland, composer of *Sea Fever*, lived in this Kent seaside town in the 1930s and wrote his *Concertino Pastorale* there?
5 Where was Henry Russell, composer of *A Life on the Ocean Wave*, aptly born on Christmas Eve, 1812?
6 For its collection of what is Finchcocks, the Georgian manor near Goudhurst, world famous?
7 What well known Yorkshire song is set to the tune, *Cranbrook*, by Canterbury born composer Thomas Clark?
8 Name the famous Genoese violinist who gave a concert at the Royal Hotel, Margate, on 27 August, 1832?
9 He had a huge following as a conductor of the Proms and was born at Bath Villas, Ashford in 1895. His name?
10 The 'singing strings' of which conductor's orchestra provided relaxing music for the millions until his death in 1980 at Tunbridge Wells.

6 GARDENS AND GARDENERS

The hop that swings so lightly
The hop that shines so brightly
Shall still be cherished rightly
By all good men and true.
Thus spake the jovial man of Kent
As through his golden hops he went
With sturdy limb and brow unbent
When autumn skies were blue.
An old Kent song

1 The gardens of which Kent 'castle' were designed by Vita Sackville-West and her husband in the 1930s?
2 Who were the designers, in 1911, of the gardens and house of The Salutation, near St Clements church, Sandwich?
3 In the gardens of Squerryes Court, Westerham, is a monument to General Wolfe, conqueror of Quebec. Why?
4 Where is there a Heaven and Hell Garden?
5 And where is there a Shakespeare Herb Garden?
6 Where do you have to go to see the National Origanum (Marjoram) Collection?
7 Who was the owner of Sholden Lodge who played for Kent Cricket Club in the 1840s and later bred 142 varieties of fuchsia for which he became world famous?
8 What does the obelisk on top of the large mound in the Dane John Gardens, Canterbury, commemorate?
9 Botanist and traveller John Tradescant the Younger, who was born at Meopham in 1608, introduced the trailing house plant that bears his name. It is?
10 In Waldershare Park, near Dover there is an eighteenth century belvedere. What is it and what purpose did it serve?

7 FAMOUS WOMEN

She wedded to live honest, but
when tried
The experiment she liked not
and so died.'

Eighteenth century lampoon verse to the subject of question 9

1 This celebrated opera singer's face was used as the model in 1896 for David the Minstrel in a stained glass window of St Mary's church, Elham. Her name?

2 Octavia Hill is buried in Holy Trinity churchyard, Crockham Hill. Of which national organisation was she one of the founders?

3 What women's service was founded in 1915 by Margaret Damer-Dawson, who was appointed its chief officer?

4 Who, at the request of her editor husband, in 1920 created Rupert Bear for the young readers of the *Daily Express?*

5 Who was the first woman to fly solo from Kent to France in April 1912?

6 Garden lovers turned every Sunday to this writer's (1892-1962) column in the *Observer* to find out what to plant, when and where?

7 Who, when she died in 1620 and was buried at Lenham, had 367 children descended from her, '16 of her own body, 114 grandchildren, 228 great-grandchildren and nine great-great-grandchildren'?

8 Name the nurse who was a probationer at a hospital in Maidstone during the typhoid epidemic of 1897-1898 and was killed by the Germans in the First World War?

9 'Notorious' Kitty Fisher was buried in her best ball gown in Benenden churchyard in 1767. Why was she 'notorious' ?

10 Who is the 'Quiet Corner' poet, buried in Sandhurst churchyard, whose morale-raising verse became immensely popular in her lifetime among people who would not normally read poetry?

8 RELIGIOSO

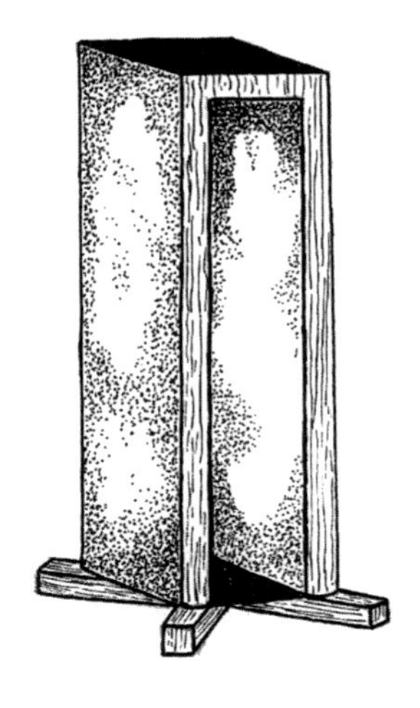

We love the windows bright
With red and yellowe paints
Presenting to our sight
The better class of Saints

Hymn parody in Evelyn Waugh's *Ronald Knox*

1. What is a hudd and for what was it used?
2. Who was known as the 'Red Dean' and why?
3. Frederick Farrar, Dean of Canterbury, 1895-1905, was more widely known as the author of what school story?
4. Which church has this request on a pillar by the door:

   Many aeroplanes fly over this church. It appears to lie on the direct route to London from abroad. Of your charity remember in prayers all those who travel by air.
5. Where was the Hatch bell foundry?
6. In which church did Nicholas Ridley order the *Te Deum* to be sung for the first time in English in England?
7. Which Kent church is dedicated to St Vincent of Saragossa, Spain's first Christian martyr?
8. Who was the archbishop murdered in his own cathedral in 1170?
9. The Danish legend of Ragnarök is depicted by a dragon, snakes, fish and crosses in Kentish ironwork on the south door of the church in which village?
10. To which quiet Kent country parish did Robert Burt diplomatically 'retire' in 1785 after secretly marrying the Prince Regent and Maria Fitzherbert at Twickenham?

9 ART AND ARCHITECTURE

Art is a lie which makes us realise the truth.
Pablo Picasso, in D Ashton's *Picasso on Art.*

1. Which of the founders of the Pre-Raphaelite Brotherhood is buried in the churchyard of All Saints, Birchington?
2. Six Victorian artists founded the Cranbrook Art Colony and specialised in painting scenes of village and country life? Score a mark for each one you can name.
3. And which one of them reputedly designed and published the first Christmas card?
4. This artist, founder of the East Kent Art Society, lived at Fordwich, exhibited at the Royal Academy, and painted local scenes as well as pictures of Morocco, Palestine and South Africa.
5. A sketch of Canterbury cathedral by this nineteenth century artist was bought by a passerby, Archbishop Manners Sutton, for £5. He was later renowned for his pictures of cattle, sheep, and rural scenes.
6. Many of his pictures are in the Slater Gallery. In which museum is it?
7. Who designed all the interior furniture, stained glass, mosaics and fittings of the new Palace of Westminster after the 1834 fire?
8. He came to Ramsgate in 1843 and designed and built The Grange on West Cliff. What did he build next door at his own expense – and for what reason?
9. The stained glass in the east window of the church at Tudeley is by a Russian artist famous in the School of Paris of the Cubist period. His name?
10. Who lived at The White House, Trottiscliffe, designed the Christ in Majesty tapestry for Coventry cathedral, and painted the controversial 80th birthday portrait of Sir Winston Churchill?

10 LITERARY LOCATIONS

There were moments when Henry was glad he was a writer, for writers could live in their own minds and didn't have to go out at all.

.Malcolm Bradbury. *Cuts*

1 The walled garden of which Kent mansion was used by Frances Hodgson Burnett as the setting for her book, *The Secret Garden,* published 1911?

2 Gad's Hill Place, Higham, was owned by which famous novelist from 1856 until his death there in 1870?

3 Why was H G Wells home at Sandgate called Spade House?

4 Why did Jane Austen often stay at Godmersham House?

5 Hole Park, Rolvenden was the home in the eighteenth century of Edward Gibbon. Of what monumental historical work was he the author?

6 In *Great Expectations* Pip refers to the graves of his five brothers in this churchyard. To which Kent churchyard and the real graves of what family was Dickens alluding?

7 Where did Ford Madox Ford describe, in 1900, as 'a place whose very name suggests storms and the horrors of the Goodwins'?

8 Who wrote *Tunbridge Toys* in 1860 in a house below Mount Ephraim, Tunbridge Wells, which is now named after him?

9 Where did Sheila Kaye-Smith set the plot of *The Loves of Joanna Godden?*

10 On the first sight of what building in Rochester did Mr Augustus Snodgrass exclaim in *The Pickwick Papers:* 'Magnificent ruin'?

11 MORE ABOUT WRITERS

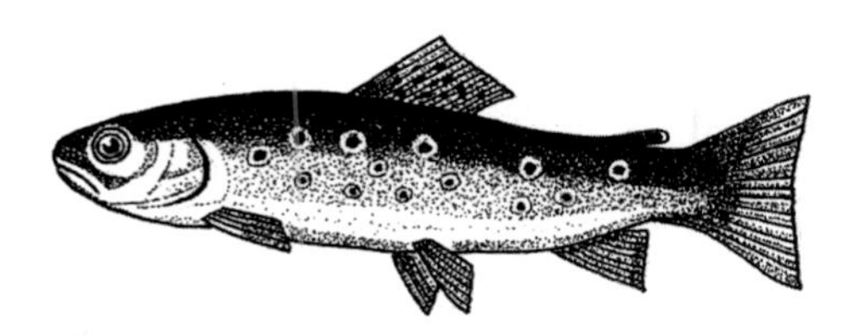

Writers tend to hang around the edges of society, designated court jesters who know they've landed the best job in court.

Alan Coren in the *Listener* 2 March 1989

1. Who wrote *In Romney Marsh* and how did he meet his death?
2. What was the title of the novel H G Wells wrote at Sandgate about a mermaid who comes ashore to find a husband?
3. Who was the writer, born at Strood, died 1893, whose numerous books, written in a popular style, opened up the world of wild plants to a wide public, particularly to children?
4. Who wrote *The Origin of Species* while living at Down House, Downe?
5. With which resort was children's author E Nesbit so delighted by its quiet seclusion that she moved there from Hythe?
6. But where was her home when she died in 1924?
7. Who was the author, creator of 007, who died of a severe haemorrhage in 1964 in Kent and Canterbury Hospital with his last stated ambition unfulfilled?
8. And what was that last ambition?
9. The author of *The Compleat Angler* was married in St Mildred's church, Canterbury in 1626 to the great great niece of Archbishop Thomas Cranmer. Name the happy couple.
10. This author, who died at Kingsgate, near Broadstairs in 1961, used twenty eight pen-names and created thirty schools, the most famous being Greyfriars. By which pen-name is he best known?

12 EDUCATION

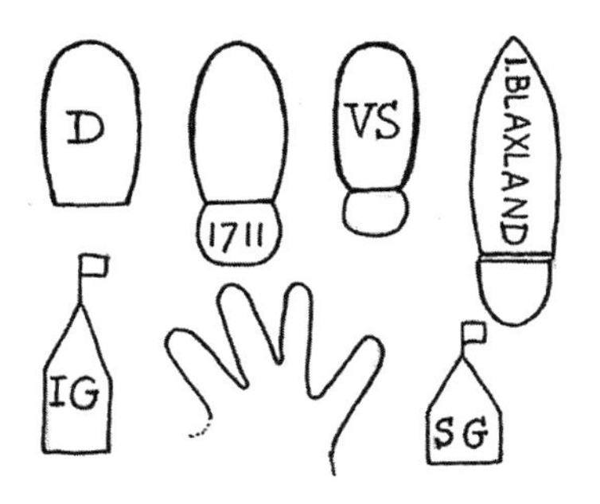

Ickham, pickham,
Penny Wickham,
Cockalorium jay,
Eggs, butter, cheese, bread,
Hick, stick, stone dead.

A Kentish children's counting rhyme

1 This is reputed to be the oldest boys' school in England. It was re-founded by Henry VIII, but originally established as a monastic school for boys in the sixth century.

2 And this school for boys was also re-founded by Henry VIII in 1550 on the dissolution of the Benedictine priory.

3 The author of *Cakes and Ale* and *Of Human Bondage*, attended Kings School, Canterbury from 1885 to 1889. Who was he?

4 Who was the Bromley High School for Girls teacher who wrote thirty eight novels about an irrepressible boy. And what was the boy's name?

5 For the education of whom was a school established at Bunce Court, Otterden, in 1933 by Frau Anna Essinger, a German teacher?

6 The sixteenth century Eastgate House in Rochester, now the Charles Dickens Centre, was used by the author as a model for what school in which book?

7 Which famous Kent public school was founded in 1432 by Sir William Sennocke?

8 Artist Vincent van Gogh was briefly a teacher in 1876 at a boys' school in Kent. Where was the school?

9 A master at Tonbridge School in the eighteenth century had a famous novelist daughter. Who were they?

10 What is macabre about the tomb in St Stephen's church, Canterbury, of Sir Roger Manwood, MP for Sandwich and founder of its grammar school?

13 STAGE AND SCREEN

Why should people go out and pay money tosee bad films when they can stay at home and see bad television for nothing?

Samuel Goldwyn.

1 Who was the famous actress, a Dame of the British Empire, who lived at Smallhythe Place, near Tenterden, from 1899 until she died 1928?

2 Some of the scenes for the film of the Howard Spring novel *Fame is the Spur* were shot at this famous Kent house?

3 What was the main location of the television series *The Darling Buds of May?*

4 Who was the librettist who lived at Tonford Manor, Thanington and wrote the lyrics for Ivor Novello's musical, *Glamorous Nights.*

5 And where is England's second oldest public theatre?

6 Where in Kent was Noel Coward's supernatural comedy *Blithe Spirit* set?

7 Where was Noel Coward living at the time he wrote it?

8 On the pedestrianised west side of Whitstable seafront is a wooden plaque bearing the words: 'Cushing's View'. Who was Cushing?

9 What was the title of the film shot in wartime Canterbury, at Chilham and other localities in the area?

10 Name the two main stars in it?

14 INNS

God made the wicked Grocer
For a mystery and a sign,
That men might shun the awful shop
And go to inns to dine.

G K Chesterton.
The Song Against Grocers.

1 Which Kent inn has a skeleton in a cupboard?
2 Where is the Ship on Shore and why is it so called?
3 Which seaside resort (it is not Broadstairs) has an inn with a Dickens Room adorned with prints and photographs relating to the author?
4 What is unique about Ye Old Crown inn at Edenbridge?
5 Why was Royal Victoria added to the name of the Bull Hotel, Rochester?
6 How did the Falstaff outside the Westgate in Canterbury benefit from pilgrims to Becket's shrine and murder scene in the cathedral?
7 At Chatham there is a pub called The Ordinary Fellow. Who was this 'ordinary fellow'?
8 Has a donkey anything to do with an inn at Ramsgate called The Blazing Donkey?
9 At Ham, near Eastry, there is another inn called The Blazing Donkey. Was a donkey involved here?
10 The Sugar Loaves at Hollingbourne, indicates by its name and inn sign that at one time it sold something in addition to beer, wine and spirits. What else did it sell?

15 CRIME AND PUNISHMENT

My object all sublime
I shall achieve in time –
To let the punishment fit the crime
The Punishment fit the crime . . .
Gilbert and Sullivan. *Mikado.*

1. The condemned cell of Canterbury's former city prison can still be visited. Where is it?
2. Who and when was the last man hanged in public on Penenden Heath, one of Kent's ancient places of execution?
3. And who was the first person executed within a prison, after public executions were abolished, having shot Edward Walsh, a Dover Priory station superintendent?
4. Where, for an admission fee, can you be a witness at a 'true' murder trial in an original courtroom and experience conditions in a Victorian prison?
5. Sir Charles Selby, whose family owned Ightham Mote, was fined £500 in 1663 for 'lewdly and indecently' doing what?
6. How was seven and a half year old Frances O'Rourke murdered by 20 year old Harold Apted in 1901 and where was her body found?
7. What happened to the Victorian artist, Richard Dadd, after he stabbed his father to death in Cobham Park in 1843?
8. Who was the fictional smuggler/vicar of Dymchurch, created by Russell Thorndike?
9. At Hothfield in the sixteenth century Gibbes, a Kentish landowner, was sentenced to be 'pressed to death'. How was such a sentence carried out?
10. What name was given to the case which involved the murder of Beatrice Mundy at 80 High Street, Herne Bay on 13 July, 1912, and the trial of her 'husband' George Joseph Smith?

16 WHAT AND WHERE?

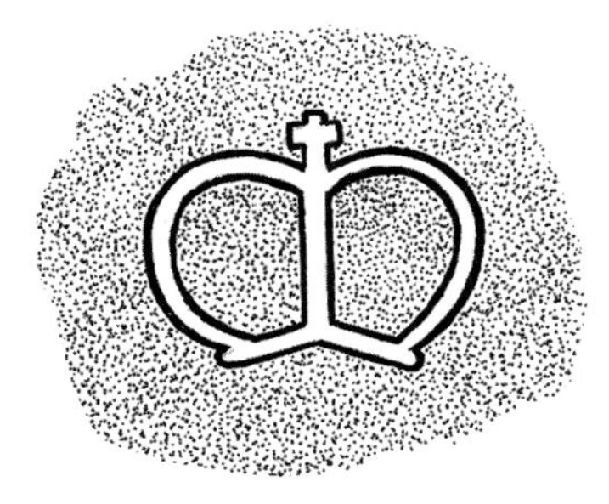

Rye, Romney and Hythe for wealth without health,
The Downs for health with poverty;
But you shall find both health and wealth
From Foreland Head to Knole and Lee.

Kent rhyme.

1 What happened in the Second World War to the 'Crown' cut into the chalk of the North Downs overlooking Wye?

2 There are two crosses cut into the white chalk of the downland slopes of Kent. One is at Lenham. Where is the second?

3 Where in Kent are the National Fruit Collections?

4 What is the Kent Ditch?

5 Where are the 22 miles of caves that were used as air raid shelters in the Second World War?

6 What was found at Charing in 1935 and why did the local population not rush for their shovels?

7 Where is Folkestone's racecourse?

8 Which river, a tributary of the Teise, was dammed in 1970 to flood three valleys on the Kent/Sussex border and created the largest lake in south east England?

9 Below the dam the same river forms the moat of what castle?

10 Hope All Saints, Midley, Eastbridge, Orgarswick and Blackmanstone on Romney Marsh are all sites of what?

17 SEASIDE AND SEASHORE

It is the drawback of all seaside places that half the landscape is unavailable for purposes of human locomotion, being covered by useless water.

Norman Douglas. *Alone.*

1 Which resort has a cliff lift with a zigzag path near it?

2 It is now a museum but what was the original purpose of the time-ball tower on Deal seafront?

3 In what year did a crew of Danish men row the *Hugin*, a vessel of traditional design, across the North Sea to commemorate the voyage made by Hengist and Horsa in AD 449?

4 For what tasty crustacea was Pegwell Bay renowned?

5 Which Kent lighthouse was the last in England to be 'demanned' and automated? And when was this done?

6 What gift of Mrs Ann Thwaytes to Herne Bay in 1837 is still benefiting both residents and visitors?

7 Which seaside resort has a model village depicting English life and complete with working transport?

8 Is The Street, Whitstable, a man-made thoroughfare?

9 From what did Seasalter, near Whitstable, take its name'?

10 Who was the Quaker glover who 'improved' Margate's first bathing machines by fitting them with a canvas umbrella or 'modesty hood'?

18 ROYALTY

God bless the King, I mean the Faith's Defender;
God Bless – no harm in blessing – the Pretender;
But who Pretender is, or who is King
God bless us all – that's quite another thing.

John Byrom.*To an Officer in the Army.*

1 Which Kent castle was the home of Anne Boleyn?
2 But where did Henry VIII and Anne Boleyn spend their honeymoon?
3 Who was the royal holidaymaker who wrote: 'To Ramsgate we used to go frequently in summer, living at Townley House and going there by steamer'?
4 Who married the 'Fair Maid of Kent' on 10 October, 1361?
5 And who was she?
6 In what town was the inn – the Queen's Arms at 12 Market Place – where in 1688 James II was held prisoner when captured while attempting to escape from England?
7 After which queen of England was Queenborough called?
8 To what, in 1858 did Queen Victoria, a sufferer from sea-sickness, give her approval 'in the name of all the ladies of England'?
9 Why did King George VI and Queen Elizabeth attend a service in Canterbury cathedral on 11 July, 1946?
10 Who was the monarch who added the Royal to Tunbridge Wells – and in what year?

19 ODDS AND ENDS

A whistling woman and a crowing hen,
Are neither good for God nor men

Old Kent saying.

1 On the map of Kent there are six 'islands'. Score a mark for each one you can name.

2 Smallhythe was once the harbour of which former 'limb' of the Federation of the Cinque Ports?

3 Why are the Neolithic 'Countless Stones' near Aylesford so called ?

4 Who was St Mildred, to whom the church at Tenterden is dedicated?

5 Why was the name of a town or city formerly painted in large white letters on the flat top of its gasometer?

6 The church at Barfreston has no tower or belfry. Where does its single bell hang?

7 Where, in 1895, did 5,000 people skate on a frozen lake, which was illuminated by coloured lights, Chinese lanterns and blazing tar barrels, to the music of the Band of the Queens Own Royal West Kent Regiment?

8 In the past there were Catch Clubs in many towns and villages in Kent. What did members of a Catch Club do?

9 In some urban areas of Kent there are even modern thoroughfares with the name Cherry Garden Road or Cherry Garden Street. Why?

10 From this village, where Chaucer's last *Canterbury Tale* was told, his pilgrims had their first sight of their destination city.

20 CASTLES AND COUNTRY HOUSES

I lived mainly at Chartwell, where I had much to amuse me . . . Thus I never had a dull or idle moment from morning to midnight.

Sir Winston Churchill. *The Gathering Storm.*

1 Which Kent castle has an antique dog collar museum?

2 What is unique about the Great Hall at Penshurst Place?

3 Walmer castle is the official residence of the Lord Warden of the Cinque Ports. Who is the present Lord Warden?

4 At Lullingstone House in 1875 Sir William Hart Dyke and two friends drew up an early form of rules for which outdoor game?

5 What, as one of his 'amusements', did Sir Winston Churchill build at Chartwell, his home near Westerham?

6 What is the purpose of the weatherboarding which is on so many of the houses in the Weald of Kent?

7 Which moated house in Kent has a Sherlock Holmes museum?

8 Northbourne Court, near Deal, has several acres of 'prospects'. What are they?

9 Tappington Hall, near Denton, was the home of the vicar who wrote *The Ingoldsby Legends* in 1840. Who was he?

10 Which medieval mansion was described by Virginia Woolf, a friend of its owner, as 'a town rather than a house?'

21 FLORA AND FAUNA

You buy some flowers for your table;
You tend them tenderly as you are able;
You fetch them water from hither and thither –
What thanks do you get for it all? They wither.

Samuel Hoffenstein.
Poems in Praise of Practically Nothing

1. What are arzey-garzeys, haazes, harves, and quicks?
2. What plants in Kent bear the names Early Spider, Late Spider, Lizard, Monkey, Lady and Green-winged?
3. What is a Kentish Glory?
4. What is the habitat of the Kentish Plover?
5. Paigle, Our Lady's Keys, Culver-Keys, are Kent country names for which wild flower?
6. Naturalist Dr John Latham in 1773 received two 'small shy birds shot by a friend on Bexley Heath'. He realised the birds were an unknown species so named them after a town in the locality. Which one?
7. In Kent Willow-Gull is another name for the golden male catkins of the Sallow or Goat Willow. Why?
8. 'Halfway down hangs one that gathers samphire, dreadful trade!' says Edgar in *King Lear* of what is now called Shakespeare's Cliff in Dover. What is samphire and for what is it used?
9. The leaves and stems of which grass – a pest in cultivated areas – were boiled or stewed and the liquid drunk to cure constipation?
10. In Kent hedgehogs, known as beetlehogs, were caught and set free inside country cottages. Why?

22 FEATURES OF THE LANDSCAPE

Above Sittingbourne the land appears to me to be as good as could possibly be . . . In short, this is a country of hop gardens, cherry, apple, pear and filbert orchards.

William Cobbett. *Rural Rides*

1. The White Cliffs of Dover inspired a song. Who was the Forces' Sweetheart who sang it?
2. What is the minnis of Stelling Minnis, near Canterbury?
3. What is the leacon of Westwell Leacon, Chart Leacon, and Warehorne Leacon?
4. And what is a ness – as in Dungeness?
5. What is a nailbourne?
6. How many of Caesar's soldiers were billeted at Caesar's Camp, overlooking Folkestone?
7. What do visitors to Bedgebury Pinetum, near Goudhurst go to see?
8. What are the Coldrum Stones, now owned by the National Trust?
9. What and where is Kit's Coty House? Can it be lived in?
10. By what name is the prehistoric communications and trade route below the North Downs through Kent to Europe known?

23 TOWNS

**Renowned Dele doth vaunt itself with Tur-
rets newly rais'd
For monuments of Caesars host, a
place in storie prais'd.**

William Lambarde.
A Perambulation of Kent.

1 Which town has the oldest street market in Kent?

2 Why was Blue Town near Sheerness so called?

3 In which town is there a shop in Week Street showing a fine example of pargetting?

4 Where is Kent's International Railway Station?

5 In the High Street of Bromley there is a large mural commemorating a locally born author. Name him?

6 Outside Chatham's railway station is a statue of Lieutenant Thomas Waghorn RN.. What trade route did he pioneer in the nineteenth century?

7 To what breed of poultry did this town give its name?

8 Where does the Kent and East Sussex Railway have its headquarters?

9 Which town is described by Arthur Mee in his *Kent* in The King's England series, as: 'The great centre point of Kent, a pivot of its history, the finest town on the Medway, a twentieth century hive of life with the fifteenth century lingering in its streets'.

10 This town, renowned for papermaking, has a museum devoted to the barge building trade and sailing barges.

24 VILLAGES

He that will not live long
Let him dwell in Murston, Tenham or Tong.

Old rhyme quoted by William Lambarde in
A Perambulation of Kent of 1570

1 What were Bearsted Diamonds' ?

2 Where is St Georges Day and May Day celebrated with a combined May Queen procession and pageant of St George and the Dragon early in May?

3 Which village, noted for the historical cricket matches played on its green, was scheduled after the Second World War for development as one of London's new satellite towns?

4 At the aerodrome in which Kent village, known as the 'home of British flight' did Sir Winston Churchill and Lord Brabazon of Tara learn to fly?

5 What was the royal connection with Milton Regis?

6 Why is a Tudor cottage in Wouldham called Purser Place?

7 Which Kent village has given its name to an apple?

8 In Faversham Road, Lenham, there is an old lock-up. What was one of its alternative uses?

9 What was revealed by First World War gunfire in the church at Lower Halstow?

10 In which village is the church known as the 'Cathedral of Romney Marsh'?

25 IN MEMORIAM

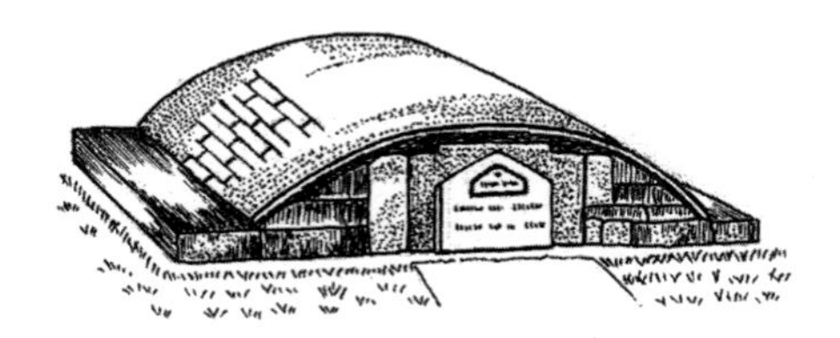

Her soul without a spot is gone to Heaven,
Her spotted body to the worms is given.
Epitaph on the headstone on the grave of Sarah Stanford, a1790 smallpox victim, in St Mary's churchyard, Hothfield,

1 Where is there a tree planted in memory of General Gordon of Khartoum?

2 On which cricket ground is the obelisk from the grave of Fuller Pilch, a former Kent player who died in 1870?

3 Where is Kent's Battle of Britain Memorial?

4 Who was the ex-Emperor of France who died at Chislehurst?

5 The Adams Memorial on Watling Street, Gillingham is a clock tower. Who was Adams?

6 Where is Nobody buried?

7 Why was one end of the vault in Pembury churchyard, in which lies the body of Anne West who died in 1803, left open until 1947?

8 For what did the forty one men and women whose names appear on a Canterbury Cross in Martyrs Field Road, Canterbury, give up their lives in between 1555 and 1558?

9 From what illness, according to the inscription on a canopied cross in St Mary's churchyard, East Farleigh, did '43 Strangers' die in September, 1849?

10 In Bethersden, Smarden and Folkestone churchyards are some oven graves. What are oven graves?

26 FOOD

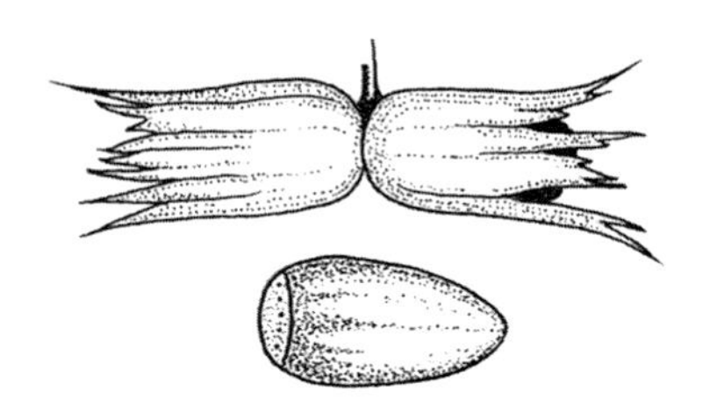

Hops and pickerel, carp and beer
Came to England all in a year.

Old rhyme

1. Cakes made with fleed were a popular Kent delicacy but what is or was fleed ?
2. In Kent fruit orchards what are scrumps?
3. Connoisseurs of seafood should not be deterred by its North Kent coastal name of ponger. What is it?
4. What was a pudding-pie and on what festive occasion was it eaten ?
5. 'Crock butter' is mentioned in many old Kent recipes. What was it?
6. Huss, Rock Salmon, Bull Huss, Robin Huss, Gurnet are all names used by Kent's fishmongers for this fish. What is its correct name?
7. Whitstable is famous for its 'natives'. Not people, what are they?
8. In Kent what is 'catsup' or 'kachup', variations of which are still being used in homes and cafes?
9. What are Kent cobs and Kentish filberts?
10. Why is the sandwich so called?

27 DO YOU KNOW?

On Monday when the sun is hot,
I wonder to myself a lot:
'Now is it true or is it not,
That what is which and which is what?'

A A Milne. *Winnie the Pooh*

1 Which American, later his country's president, while living in England worshipped in the Unitarian chapel at Tenterden in 1783 ?

2 What job did a muddie do?

3 Who, or what, was a hoveller ?

4 Name the road, most of it lying on the original Roman foundations, that runs in a straight line, except for one bend, from near Lympne to Canterbury ?

5 In which year was the electrification of the railway between London and the Kent coast completed?

6 And when was the New Kingsferry Bridge, linking the Isle of Sheppey and the mainland, opened?

7 What coastal feature is a Wantsum?

8 Which American composer conducted concerts of his famous marches at Chatham, Maidstone and Tunbridge Wells in 1905?

9 What are Fuggles, Apple Puddings, Golden Tips, Goldings, Pretty Wills and Late Red Bine?

10 Anthony Pig, Daniel, Dolly and Runtlet, are all Kent country names for which creature?

28 MILITARY AND MUSEUM PIECES

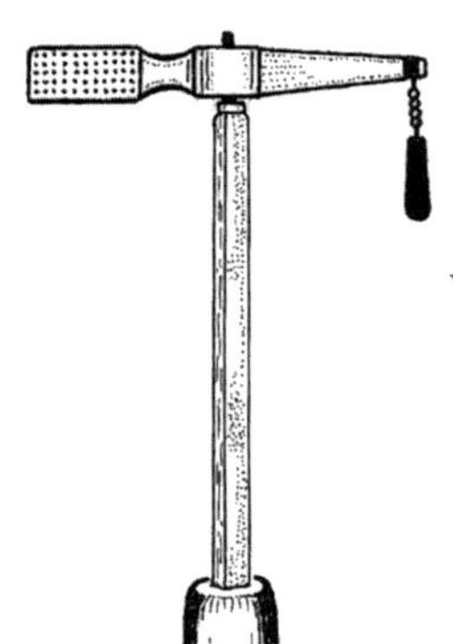

I prefer our military past. The harm's done and there it is. As for being a General, well at the age of four with paper hats and wooden swords we're all Generals. Only some of us never grow out of it.

Peter Ustinov. *Romanoff and Juliet*

1 On Offham's village green stands what is reputed to be the last surviving quintain. What was its purpose?

2 What was the name of Napoleon's favourite charger and where is he buried? A clue is a type of orange.

3 In which Kent castle can you see 'Queen Elizabeth's Pocket Pistol' ?

4 Which Kent regiment was nicknamed the 'Dirty Half Hundred' and why?

5 What was the purpose of the Grand Shaft, Snargate Street, Dover?

6 Where is the Royal Engineers' Museum of Military Engineering?

7 This was one of the main, and certainly the best known, RAF fighter stations in the Battle of Britain. Its name?

8 In the Buffs museum is the silver Albuhera Group depicting a soldier on horseback striking a soldier on foot with his sword. That soldier is Lieutenant Matthew Latham, who lost an arm and part of his face doing what?

9 Where is the Buffs (East Kent Regiment) museum?

10 What was Operation Pluto and what do the initials stand for?

KENT PICTURE QUIZ

1 **What is the name of this unusual type of steeple on the church of St Mary of Charity, Faversham?**

2 **At which Kent port is this obelisk and why was it erected by the harbour trustees and the inhabitants?**

3 To which railway town in Kent was this tank, now classed as a listed building, presented in 1919 and why?

4 Charles Dickens request to be buried on this site was refused. What and where is it?

5 **This memorial, by the designer of the Cenotaph in Whitehall, is in gardens in which Kent market town?**

6

A murder most foul was committed in this house in 1551 and it became the plot of a Jacobean drama which is still performed. Who was killed and what is the title of the play.

7 **For what was this platform approached by three steps at the entrance to Crundale churchyard intended to be used?**

8 Where is this Italianate conservatory which was built in 1805 by an Admiral for grapevine he brought back from Corsica?

9 Where and for how long has this larger than life boy been waiting for the tide to come in so he can sail his boat?

10 Seeing is beelieving. What is this in the wall of the Kent Memorial Garden at Canterbury?

11 ‘Ullo! ‘Ullo! Wot‘s goin‘ on ‘ere? And where? And why?

12 **What is unusual about the construction of the church at Bicknor among the chalk hills south of Sittingbourne?**

13 **Efforts are being made to preserve this paddle steamer which saved 7,000 servicemen from Dunkirk. What is her name?** *Photo: Noreen Chambers.*

14 **This is the oldest building in Kent, possibly the oldest in the country. For what purpose was it built and by whom?**

15 **Where is this chalybeate spring and who made drinking its waters fashionable in the seventeenth century?** *Photo: Diana Bailey*

16 **Who were the smack boys and why did they need this home in Ramsgate?**

17

What is the link between this bust and the sculptures on the Dover seafront pictured below?

18 What and where is this civic building, said to be the smallest of its kind in England?

19 Sir John Spilman's tomb is in this church. What industry did he pioneer? *Photo: Diana Bailey.*

20 In which churchyard are these stocks? *Photo: Diana Bailey.*

ANSWERS

1 KENT BOOK OF RECORDS

1 It issued the first regular railway passenger season tickets in 1834.
2 In the Agricultural Showground at Tunbridge Wells on 15 October, 1895.
3 Near the castle at Dover. The spot is marked by a granite outline of his monoplane set in the turf.
4 The cherry.
5 South Foreland. Marconi set up his wireless apparatus there and transmitted a message to the East Goodwin lightship.
6 At Lenham. Dr Stephen Gray, who lived at Otterden Place, was the successful experimenter.
7 Margate. The Tom Thumb Theatre has a stage measuring 7ft by 10ft.
8 In 1935 in a garden pond at Stone-in-Oxney. The female's head and body can measure up to 5 inches; the male's up to 3fi inches.
9 St Mary Magdalene's church, Cobham. They are of the Cobham family and cover two centuries of the late Middle Ages.
10 At Dartford, in what was then known as Baldwyn's Park, on 3 November 1894.

2 FAMOUS MEN

1 George Bernard Shaw.
2 Richard Trevithick
3 He was made a Freeman of the Borough.
4 The circulation of the blood.
5 Sir Alec Rose.
6 Mick Jagger, in 1943.
7 Beau Nash.
8 Sir Thomas More, Henry VIII's Lord Chancellor. His head was rescued by his daughter, Margaret Roper, after he was beheaded on Tower Hill in 1535.
9 St John Fisher. He opposed Henry's divorce from Catherine of Aragon and was beheaded on Tower Hill for refusing to take the Oath of Supremacy. He was canonised in 1935.
10 Sir Malcolm Campbell who died in 1948. He held the land speed record of 310mph in 1935 and in 1939 the water speed record 141.7mph

3 CHURCHES

1 The south boundary wall, built in 1922, is serpentine in shape, curving in and out along its entire length.
2 St Michael the Archangel, Smarden, because of its wide scissor-beamed roof.
3 The link is Lawrence Washington, who died in 1619. He is related to American president, George Washington, and his coat of arms on his memorial by the south door shows the stars and stripes of the embryonic American flag.
4 It is separate from the church, because it was thought the foundations in marshy ground would not support both the tower and belfry.
5 A hinged metal plate, usually of brass, attached to a wall and engraved on both sides. In this example there is a Latin inscription to Sir James Dering, who died in 1532, on one side and an English inscription to Philemon Downdall, who died in 1660, on the other.
6 To bake wafers for mass and to heat charcoal for the incense burners.
7 St Mary's, Patrixbourne. The eighteen panels of enamelled glass date from 1538.
8 St Dunstan's, Cranbrook.
9 Human skulls and bones, exhumed when new graves were dug in the churchyard.
10 Because most of those who drank the spa water and funded the building of the church were royalists – and Henrietta Maria, wife of Charles I, recuperated there after giving birth to the future Charles II.

4 MIXED BAG

1 The Belisha beacon. He was Minister of Transport from 1934 to 1937 when pedestrian crossings, marked at the kerbside with lights in orange globes on poles were introduced.
2 William Wordsworth in his *To the Men of Kent.*
3 The largest country home for orphans in Dr Barnado's organisation. It was opened in 1886 at Hawkhurst.
4 Edward Bainbridge Copnall.
5 It is a block of stone, brick or wood with steps on one side. The horse would be made to 'joss' – that is come close to the block, so its rider could climb the steps and mount more easily than from the ground.

6 Its breed of hardy sheep.
7 Doddington.
8 A cat – because it kept down rats and mice.
9 Cricket bats.
10 A 6ft 9inch long sturgeon weighing 100 lbs.

5 MUSIC AND MUSICIANS

1 Peter Warlock.
2 Smallpox
3 In Canterbury cathedral, where his bust still gazes across the nave.
4 Deal.
5 Sheerness.
6 Early keyboard instruments.
7 On Ilkley Moor Baht 'at'.
8 Paganini.
9 Sir Malcolm Sargent.
10 Mantovani.

6 GARDENS AND GARDENERS

1 Sissinghurst Castle, near Cranbrook.
2 The house by Sir Edward Lutyens, the gardens by Gertrude Jekyll.
3 He was a friend of the owners, the Warde family, and while in the garden received his first commission from a Government courier.
4 In the Broadview Gardens of Hadlow Agricultural College. They are open to the public.
5 Every herb Shakespeare mentions in his plays is in the garden of Stoneacre Manor House, a National Trust property at Otham.
6 To the Iden Croft Herb Garden at Staplehurst.
7 Edward R Banks. One cultivar of 1876 was called Beauty of Kent.
8 The designing and laying out of the gardens, with their Lime Tree Walk, as a public pleasure ground in 1790.
9 *Tradescantia virginia.*
10 A belvedere was a sort of useful folly. It was a structure, this one 60ft high, with steps inside it which could be climbed to obtain a view of the surrounding countryside from the summit.

7 FAMOUS WOMEN

1 Coloratura soprano Madame Adelina Patti.
2 The National Trust.
3 The Women' s Police Service.
4 Mary Tourtel.
5 Harriet Quimby, in her Bleriot monoplane.
6 Victoria Sackville West.
7 Mary Honywood. She was married at 16 and died aged 93.
8 Nurse Edith Cavell.
9 She was a famous London courtesan. To gain respectability she married John Norris, a Kent landowner, but died a year later, possibly poisoned by the white lead in her make-up.
10 'Patience Strong' – Winifred Cushing, who died in 1990.

8 RELIGIOSO

1 It is a wooden, portable shelter, like a sentry box. It was carried to the graveside so the parson could stand inside it and keep dry while conducting an interment in wet weather.
2 Dr Hewlett Johnson, Dean of Canterbury 1931-1963, because he favoured Communism.
3 He was the author of the once-popular partly autobiographical school story *Eric, or Little by Little.*
4 Hollingbourne.
5 Broomfield, near Ulcombe.
6 St Martin's church, Herne. For being 'corrupt and naughty' Queen Mary had him burnt at the stake in 1555.
7 Littlebourne.
8 Archbishop Thomas à Becket at Canterbury.
9 Staplehurst.
10 St Mary Hoo.

9 ART AND ARCHITECTURE

1 Dante Gabriel Rossetti who died in 1882.
2 The artists are: George Hardy, Frederick Hardy, Thomas Webster, John Callcott Horsley, A E Mulready and George O'Neill.
3 John Callcott Horsley in 1846.

4 Alfred Palmer. He died in 1951.
5 Thomas Sidney Cooper who lived at Vernon Holme near Harbledown.
6 The Royal Museum at the Beaney Institute, Canterbury.
7 Augustus Welby Northmore Pugin.
8 St Augustine's church so he could be buried there.
9 Marc Chagall.
10 Graham Sutherland

10 LITERARY LOCATIONS

1 Great Maytham Hall, Rolvenden. The garden is open to the public in the summer.
2 Charles Dickens.
3 Wells' architect, C F Voysey, who designed and built it, wanted to put a heart-shaped letter plate on the front door. Wells objected and they compromised on a spade.
4 It belonged to her brother, Edward.
5 *The Decline and Fall of the Roman Empire*, published 1776 to 1788.
6 St James churchyard at Cooling which has the thirteen graves of the Comport children.
7 Deal.
8 William Makepiece Thackeray. The house is called Thackeray House.
9 On Romney Marsh.
10 Rochester castle.

11 MORE ABOUT WRITERS

1 John Davidson. He committed suicide by walking into the sea on the Cornish coast.
2 *The Sea Lady.*
3 Anne Pratt.
4 Charles Darwin.
5 Dymchurch.
6 Jesson St Mary where she lived in two bungalows, one called the Long Boat, second the Jolly Boat, connected by a passage called the Suez Canal.
7 Ian Fleming.

8 To be made Captain of the Royal St Georges Golf Club. He died two days before the ceremony.
9 Izaak Walton and Rachel Floud.
10 Frank Richards. His real name was Charles Harold St John Hamilton.

12 EDUCATION

1 The King's School, Canterbury.
2 The King's School, Rochester.
3 William Somerset Maugham.
4 Richmal Crompton. The boy was William Brown.
5 German-Jewish children who had fled from the Nazi education system in Germany. The New Herrlingen School continued until 1948.
6 As Westgate House Seminary for Young Ladies, in *The Pickwick Papers.*
7 Sevenoaks School.
8 6 Royal Road, Ramsgate.
9 The Reverend George Austen, father of Jane Austen.
10 At the base of the tomb, on which is his bust, is a full size replica of a skeleton lying on its back. The tomb was made in his lifetime, to his instructions.

13 STAGE AND SCREEN

1 Dame Ellen Terry
2 Knole
3 Pluckley and the surrounding countryside.
4 Christopher Hassall.
5 At Margate. The Theatre Royal opened on 27 June, 1787.
6 Around Aldington and the Romney Marsh area.
7 Goldenhurst Farm, Aldington, where he also wrote *This Happy Breed* and *Present Laughter.*
8 Peter Cushing, the stage and screen actor who appeared in many horror films. He lived nearby for many years and enjoyed the view across the Medway estuary.
9 *The Canterbury Tale.*
10 Sheila Sim and Eric Portman.

14 INNS

1 The Woolpack Inn, Benover, Yalding. It is in a cupboard under the stairs.
2 Marine Parade, Sheerness. In 1858 the *Lucky Escape* ran aground there and the barrels of cement in its cargo were rescued. When dried the barrel shaped blocks were used to build a grotto beside the inn.
3 The British Lion, the Bayle, Folkestone, which Dickens frequented on visits to the town.
4 It has an inn sign that spans the main street.
5 To mark the occasion when Princess Victoria had to spend a night there when Rochester bridge was damaged in a storm.
6 When pilgrims arrived late and found the Westgate and other city gates closed the inn provided them with accommodation.
7 King George V. During the 1935 Jubilee celebrations he was amazed at the display of loyalty by his subjects. 'For, after all, I am but an ordinary fellow,' he said.
8 Yes. In the nineteenth century a donkey was being groomed in the stables of the Alexandra Arms and its coat caught fire as some straggly hairs were being singed off with a lighted taper. Customers doused the flames and the donkey survived. The inn was renamed soon after that occurrence.
9 Incredibly, yes. A barn nearby caught fire and the donkey kept in it by a gipsy escaped with its coat alight but had to be put down.
10 Groceries. Sugar used to be sold in 'loaves' or blocks and these were often pictured on grocers' trade signs.

15 CRIME AND PUNISHMENT

1 In the Westgate.
2 John Dyke in 1830 for firing a hayrick. He vowed he was innocent and this proved true when another man made a death bed confession.
3 Thomas Wells, an 18 year old carriage cleaner. He was executed in Maidstone prison in August, 1868.
4 At Dover, in the Old Town Gaol.
5 Running the length of London's Fleet Street naked, possibly for a wager.
6 After sexually assaulting her he used a knife to sever her left jugular vein. It was still entangled in her hair when he dumped the body in Vauxhall Pond.

7 He was found guilty of murder and confined in Broadmoor Asylum, where for forty years, until his death in 1886, he painted pictures which now command large sums.
8 Dr Syn.
9 The convicted man was laid flat on his back and a heavy stone weight placed on his chest so he could not move. He was given only bread and water on alternate days until he died.
10 The Bride in the Bath murder.

16 WHAT AND WHERE

1 It was covered with foliage so it was not visible from the air for use as a navigational aid by enemy aircraft pilots.
2 At Shoreham. As at Lenham it is a memorial to the dead of two world wars.
3 At Brogdale Farm, Faversham.
4 A natural feature, improved by man, which forms the south west boundary between Kent and Sussex.
5 At Chislehurst. There are daily guided tours of the 1fi miles of caves that are open to the public.
6 Gold and silver, but in uneconomic small quantities – half an ounce of gold and 23 ounces of silver per ton of clay.
7 At Stanford, although the railway station is named Westenhanger.
8 The Bewl River. Bewl Water at Lamberhurst now covers 770 acres and the scenic Round Water route path is 12fi miles long.
9 Scotney Castle.
10 Lost villages. The sites of Hope All Saints and Eastbridge are indicated by fragments of their ruined churches.

17 SEASIDE AND SEASHORE

1 Folkestone.
2 It gave a time signal daily to ships in the Channel. At 1 pm, activated by an electric signal from Greenwich Observatory, the large black ball on top of the roof dropped down the mast. The time check enabled seafarers to calculate their longtitude.
3 In 1949.
4 Shrimps.

5 North Foreland, in 1998.
6 The clock and its tower on the sea front.
7 Ramsgate, on the West Cliff.
8 No. The Street or the Street Stones, is a bank of shingle extending about a mile out to sea.
9 From the seasalterne or salthouse where the sea salt from the medieval saltpans was processed.
10 Benjamin Beale, a native of the town.

18 ROYALTY

1 Hever Castle.
2 The now ruined Shurland Hall, near Eastchurch on the Isle of Sheppey.
3 Queen Victoria.
4 Edward, the Black Prince, son of Edward III.
5 His cousin, Joan, Countess of Kent.
6 At Faversham. The king was seized by local fishermen when the vessel in which he was escaping ran aground in the Swale.
7 Queen Philippa, wife of Edward III. She visited the town, then called Bynnee, in 1366 and it was renamed in her honour.
8 The proposal for a Channel Tunnel that had been mooted by French engineer, Aimé Thomé
9 In thanksgiving for the preservation of the cathedral from enemy action in the Second World War.
10 Edward VII, in 1909.

19 ODDS AND ENDS

1 Thanet, Oxney, Sheppey and its two smaller 'islands' of Elmley and Harty, and the Isle of Grain.
2 Tenterden.
3 According to local legend it is because they are arranged in such a way that it is impossible for anyone accurately to count them.
4 St Mildred, abbess of a convent at Minster in Thanet. She was 'a comforter for all in affliction'.
5 So that in the days before air traffic control the pilots of aircraft passing overhead could check their position.
6 In the branches of an ancient yew tree beside the church.
7 At Mote Park, Maidstone.

8 Similar to close harmony singing. A catch was a musical round for three or more male voices.
9 It is a peculiarity of Kent that crops such as cherries and hops were grown in 'gardens'. Such street names indicate that at one time cherries were grown in the area.
10 Harbledown.

20 CASTLES AND COUNTRY HOUSES

1 Leeds castle, near Maidstone.
2 The 64 feet long, 60 feet high room is virtually unchanged since it was built in the fourteenth century.
3 Queen Elizabeth, the Queen Mother.
4 Lawn tennis. Not having a net they used a ladder supported on two barrels instead.
5 A length of brick wall.
6 To throw rain from the sides of the property and so improve the waterproofing and interior warmth.
7 Groombridge Place, near Tunbridge Wells.
8 Tiers of brick terraces which provide views over the garden and surrounding countryside.
9 The Reverend Richard Harris Barham.
10 Knole.

21 FLORA AND FAUNA

1 They are names for haws, the berries of the hawthorn
2 Wild orchids.
3 A moth.
4 The seashore. It is a wading sea-bird.
5 The cowslip.
6 Dartford. They were Dartford Warblers..
7 Because they resemble the yellow down of a young gosling, called a gull in Kent.
8 An aromatic plant the leaves of which were used to make pickle.
9 Couch grass.
10 So theywould rid the rooms of beetles and other insects.

22 FEATURES OF THE LANDSCAPE

1 Dame Vera Lynn.
2 A wide tract of land, partly copse, partly open common.
3 A wet, swampy stretch of common land.
4 A point, cape, promontory, headland or foreland.
5 An intermittent stream that surfaces when underground springs become overfull.
6 None. The earthworks rise in the centre of a natural chalk escarpment, ringed by an Iron Age camp rampart. It has no association with Caesar.
7 A collection of pines and related conifers, some rare, in an open-air cultivation 'laboratory' supervised by the Forestry Commission.
8 Remains of a New Stone Age communal burial place with a circle of large stones round it, near Trottiscliffe.
9 An exposed stone central chamber of a Neolithic burial mound, with capstone, north-east of Aylesford close to Bluebell Hill.I t cannot be lived in.
10 The Pilgrims Way.

23 TOWNS

1 Faversham. It is recorded in the Domesday survey of 1086
2 Because it was originally inhabited by dockyard workers who painted their wooden houses blue, using Admiralty paint.
3 Maidstone. Pargetting is a moulded and painted type of plasterwork on the frontage of a building.
4 Ashford.
5 H G Wells.
6 The overland route to India.
7 Orpington.
8 Tenterden.
9 Maidstone.
10 The DolphinYard Sailing Barge Museum, Crown Quay Lane, Sittingbourne.

24 VILLAGES

1 Very hard, small, white crystals in the sand deposits around Bearsted, that took a high polish, and were used by jewellers as brilliants in semi-precious settings.

2 Bredhurst. All the children of the Church of England primary school take part, as they have for at least a century.
3 Meopham.
4 Eastchurch.
5 It is an ancient royal borough and a number of Saxon kings lived there.
6 Because it was owned by Walter Burke, the purser who cradled the dying Nelson in his arms after Trafalgar.
7 Allington. The Allington Pippin was introduced in 1896 by George Bunyard.
8 As the mortuary for the village workhouse.
9 A twelfth century Norman lead tub-font. Vibration from gunfire caused the plaster with which it had been covered to crack and fall away.
10 Lydd.

25 IN MEMORIAM

1 In the south-west corner of the old section of Canterbury city cemetery, Westgate Court Avenue. The silver lime, planted in 1885, was damaged in the 1987 storm.
2 St Lawrence ground, Canterbury, by the main entrance.
3 On a clifftop at Capel-le-Ferne, between Dover and Folkestone, is the seated figure of a 1940 fighter pilot.
4 Napoleon III, in January, 1873, at Camden Place.
5 Williams Adams was one of the first Europeans to visit Japan. He spent 20 years there, founded the Japanese Navy and built ships for it in western style. He died there in 1620.
6 In Otham churchyard. He was William Stevens, an author who used the penname 'Nobody'.
7 She had a dream that while in a trance she had been buried alive so her will instructed that there was to be no lid on her coffin, one end of the vault was to be left open and food and drink be placed there by her butler for a year after her death.
8 For their religious beliefs. They were Protestants who refused to embrace the Catholic faith in the reign of Queen Mary.
9 Cholera. 'Strangers' was the Kent name for London's East Enders who annually came to pick hops.
10 A style of burial vault with arched brickwork covered with cement or turf.

26 FOOD

1 Fleed was the fat of a pig which was rendered into lard.
2 Small fruit, usually apples and pears, left on the trees because they were of unsaleable size.
3 The edible crab.
4 A flat tart, made like a cheese cake, with a raised crust to hold ground rice or custard, sprinkled with currants. It was eaten at Easter.
5 Salt butter put into earthenware crocks to keep fresh for use in winter.
6 The Lesser-spotted Dogfish.
7 Oysters.
8 A Kentish ketchup made with mushrooms, salt, pepper, ginger, cloves and bay leaves.
9 Nuts.
10 Because keen gambler John Montagu, Earl of Sandwich, did not want to interrupt his time at the tables for meals. He told his servant to put slices of beef between slices of buttered bread for him to take to eat while he was playing.

27 DO YOU KNOW?

1 Benjamin Franklin.
2 Dug mud from the Medway mudflats at low tide. It was used in making cement powder.
3 A coastal boatman who did marine odd-jobbing and general repair work.
4 Stone Street.
5 1961
6 13 April, 1960, by Princess Marina.
7 A sea passage, existing in Roman and Saxon times, which has silted up and linked previously separated areas of land.
8 John Philip Sousa.
9 They are varieties of hops.
10 The smallest, weakest piglet in a litter.

28 MILITARY AND MUSEUM PIECES

1 A tilting post which mounted knights, armed with lances, could use to practice jousting.
2 Jaffa. The horse was named after the Battle of Jaffa Port of 1799 and is buried in Glassenbury Park, Cranbrook.

3 Dover castle grounds. It is a large cannon made in Utrecht in 1544 and given to the queen by the Dutch in recognition of the assistance she rendered them against the Spanish.
4 The Royal West Kent Regiment. Their tunics had black facings and if the soldiers wiped their perspiring brows on their sleeves on hot days the black dye gave their faces an unwashed appearance.
5 It was built to allow soldiers in the garrison at the clifftop to deploy rapidly to the harbour below.
6 In the Ravelin Building, Prince Arthur Road, Gillingham.
7 Biggin Hill.
8 Saving the King's Colour from the enemy during the Battle of Albuhera in Spain. He tore it from its pike and stuffed it into his tunic as he collapsed before being rescued.
9 The Royal Museum, Beaney Institute, Canterbury.
10 The laying of more than 60 miles of pipeline from Dungeness to the Calais area to supply fuel after the D-Day invasion. Pipe Line Under The Ocean.

29 PICTURE QUIZ

1 A lantern steeple. This one is copied from St Dunstans-in-the-East, London.
2 Ramsgate – in gratitude for George IV 'condescending to select' the port for his embarkation for Hanover and for his 'happy return' in November 1821.
3 Ashford for the town's 'service to the nation' particularly by its inhabitants high purchase of war loans.
4 The 'island' graveyard opposite the west door of Rochester cathedral.
5 In Brenchley Gardens, Maidstone. It is dedicated to two world wars' dead of the Queens Own Royal West Kent Regiment and is about two thirds the size of Sir Edward Lutyens' Whitehall Cenotaph.
6 Thomas Arden, the mayor of Faversham, was murdered in his house, 80 Abbey Street. *Arden of Faversham* is the play.
7 By horsemen, as a mounting block.
8 In the King George VI Memorial Park, Ramsgate. It was built by Admiral Lord Keith and has unusual curved, scalloped-edge glass panes that overlap like fish scales.
9 In Herne Bay. *The Boy with the Boat* sculpture by Paula Haughney was erected in 1993 as part of an £8 million seafront improvement scheme.
10 A bee bole – an aperture in a wall in which stood a bee skep.

11 Figures of an escaping prisoner and a Victorian policeman placed outside the Old Town Goal at Dover to publicise the display within.
12 The interior walls are made of chalk blocks, an unstable material, and they were faced with flints in the mid-nineteenth century to protect them from weather damage.
13 The *Medway Queen.*
14 The Pharos by Dover castle. The survivor of two beacon towers built by the Romans to guide their ships into port.
15 In the Pantiles at Tunbridge Wells. Lord North took samples of the water back to London with him in 1606 and had them tested. He was told they had 'health giving properties' and he and his friends regularly 'took the cure' after bouts of dissipation.
16 They were employed on the fishing smacks to do chores. Those who were orphans or 'bad boys' were accommodated in this home next to the seamen's church.
17 The bust is of Captain Matthew Webb, in 1875 the first man to swim the English Channel. The sculptures by Ray Smith on Dover seafront, commemorate Dover's Channel swimming history.
18 The thirteenth century court house and town hall of Fordwich..
19 Papermaking. In 1586 he started at Dartford what is believed to have been the first commercially successful papermill in the country. His effigy in gilded armour is on his tomb in Holy Trinity Church, Dartford.
20 St Michael and All Angels, Marden.

Front cover: The former King's School Bookshop in Palace Street. There are several theories as to why it leans. The most likely is that extra fireplaces were inserted in the nineteenth century making the stack top heavy and pulling the seventeenth century timber frame out of true.

Title page: The Invicta monument in St Peter and St Paul's churchyard at Swanscombe.

Back cover: The thirteenth century gatehouse and drum towers of Tonbridge Castle.

Cover and title page photos: Diana Bailey

KEY TO ILLUSTRATIONS ON SPECIFIC SUBJECTS

Quiz

1 Marsh Frog (*Rana ridibunda*).
2 Shield on the tomb of Edward, the Black Prince.
3 Human skulls and bones, Hythe.
4 Belisha beacons.
5 A harpsichord of 1725.
6 Fuchsia.
7 E Nesbit's graveboard, St. Mary-in-the-Marsh.
8 A hudd.
9 The Grange, West Cliff, Ramsgate.
10 Rochester castle
11 Brown trout.
12 King's schoolboys' graffiti in Canterbury Cathedral cloisters.
13 Theatre Royal, Margate.
14 Part of the folly 'Ship on Shore' at Sheernesss.

Quiz

15 The Westgate, Canterbury
16 Wye Crown.
17 The time-ball tower, Deal.
18 The Guildhall, Faversham,
19 The 'Leper' church at Harbledown.
20 Dog Collar museum exhibit
21 Cowslip.
22 Kit's Coty House, near Aylesford
23 Medway sailing barge
24 Norman tub-font in Lower Halstow church.
25 Oven grave in St Mary's churchyard, Folkestone.
26 Kentish filberts
27 Hops
28 The quintain at Offham.

BIBLIOGRAPHY

Kent, A Shire County Guide by John Vigar. Shire Publications 1988.
Kent by T A Bushell. Barracuda Books 1976.
Kent Inns and their Signs by Michael David Mirams, Meresborough Books 1987.
The Kent Village Book by Alan Bignell. Countryside Books, 1992.
The River and the Downs, Kent's Unsung Corner by Michael Baldwin, Gollancz 1984.